INSPIRATIONS WEEKLY WRITING JOURNAL

52 Writing Prompts for Short Stories

Copyright Alphabet Publishing 2020

ISBN: 978-1-948492-47-8 (print)
978-1-948492-53-9 (ebook)

Cover photo by tanyadzu/DepositPhotos. Cover font: Homemade Apple/Font Diner.

For permission requests, write to the publisher "ATTN: Permissions", at the address below:

Alphabet Publishing

1204 Main Street #172

Branford, CT 06405 USA

info@alphabetpublishingbooks.com

www.alphabetpublishingbooks.com

Discounts on class sets and bulk orders available upon inquiry.

Any way you want!

This book is full of ideas, one for every week of the year! But an idea alone is not a story. You need to build a story. That means you need to find a way to show how the idea affects people's lives. So a story has characters. Events happen to those characters. They react in some way. Eventually, there is some kind of resolution.

The guiding questions under each prompt are meant to help you find the story from the idea. Feel free to pick and chose the questions that seem intriguing to you or add your own. Generally, with any idea it's always good to think about three things:

1. What's the best thing that could happen?

2. What's the worst thing that could happen?

3. What is the mood of my story?

4. What situation/characters/actions would best show the idea behind my story?

> In a world where robots have replaced humans as workers, for example, the best thing that can happen is that the robots work extremely well. Every need is taken care of and people have free time to do anything they want: travel, create art, be with friends and loved ones. Human culture is more advanced and developed than ever before.
>
> The worst thing that could happen is the robots see themselves as slaves and start a secret revolution. They have all the tools and weapons they need and are faster and stronger than people. Or someone hacks into the computer that controls the robots and uses them to steal, murder, go to war against another country.
>
> I like the idea of someone hacking the robots, so I think I'll write a mystery about robots committing perfect crimes, and we have

to find out who the mastermind behind it is. So I think a good situation would be police investigating crimes against a very rich person who has many robot servants. This person spends all their time mastering different kinds of art, but has discovered their robot servants disappear for long periods of time and are in fact killing people.

Now we've got the beginning of a story.

STORY STRUCTURES

Once you've developed your idea, it's time to flesh it out. Having a structure helps make it easier. Following a familiar structure also helps the reader. A good story should be easy to follow and having a predictable outline helps. Of course, that doesn't mean you can't have plenty of surprises as well.

The figure below outlines a typical story structure. You may have seen a similar chart before. The names and numbers of the different stages may vary, but the basic concept remains con-

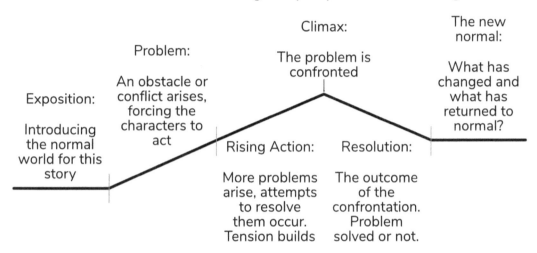

stant in most fiction, particularly in the Western world:

Essentially, the story starts out **introducing your world. Who are your characters and what is their life like?** For a science-fiction or fantasy story, this may require some explanation. Many stories begin with a stereotypical moment that illustrates concisely who your characters are: A shy girl awkwardly asking a boy out and making a fool of herself; a smart and tough businesswoman running a meeting where she exhibits her knowledge and stops people who try to take advantage of her; a robot teacher running a class and demonstrating its ability to know everything and also read biometric data to identify confused students.

Next, **a problem of some kind** arises. It may be an event, the introduction of a new character, the main character's desire for something, a need to find something out, or a mystery to be solved. But something happens that changes the status quo. The character has some kind of problem to solve. **The main action of the story is the character attempting to solve this problem and succeeding or failing.** The problem may also intensify or the character may face new problems.

Eventually, there is **a climax where the problem is confronted**. Often, the main character makes a kind of choice that leads to this climax. The hero decides to confront the bad guy, the detective brings the suspects together to find the criminal, or the loser decides to finally enroll in business school. Sometimes the climax is also preordained: a final exam, a last chance before the bomb goes off, or a work deadline.

After the climax, whatever happens, there is **a resolution that ends the conflict** in one way or another. The problems may all be solved or only partially solved. The character gains what they want or only part of it. The goal turns out to be undesirable. The cost of getting it was too high. The real treasure was the friends we made along the way. But in some way, the main problem that started the story must come to an end.

Finally, we get an idea of how the characters or the world has changed. The hero got stronger, wiser, richer, or fell in love. The villain was defeated or learned their lesson. The world was repaired, the corrupt leaders were replaced, the forest regrew, and the war ended. Something happened as a result of this story. **The end of the story shows us what that new normal is**.

THE WRITING PROCESS

Hopefully, you now have a good idea of what you want to write. The writing process is pretty simple: outline, write, revise, rewrite. Here's a good way to do that.

Outline

A simple way to plan your story is to write down:

1. The prompt on the top of a piece of paper

2. The context, setting, and any other important global details under that.

3. List the names of the main characters and their relationships to each other. You may also want to sketch out the basics of what will happen to them.

4. Now write the following headers on the left side of the page, leaving room between them:

   a. Exposition

   b. Problem

   c. Rising Action

   d. Climax

   e. Resolution

   f. New Normal

For each heading sketch out what will happen. How will introduce your world? What will the problem be? How will the action intensify, climax, and ultimately resolve? And what will change?

Write

Try to write without thinking too much about spelling and grammar. Let the ideas and words flow. Be sure to consult your outline and make sure you are staying on track. While writing, however, you may find that you come up with a new idea. Or that your plan doesn't work as well as you thought. That's ok. Go back to your outline, revise it, and continue writing.

Revise

You may want to spell-check and edit for grammar and word choice immediately. If at all possible, try to put your writing away for some time before you do any more editing than that. That way you come back to it with fresh eyes. Sometimes we don't notice problems with our writing because we know what we mean in our heads.

Rewrite

Then revise and rewrite and revise and rewrite, as much as you need to.

Share

This may be part of the revision process. It's a good idea to get someone else to look at your work and give you feedback, even edit it for you. However, it's also motivating to share with another person. Knowing someone is going to read your work helps keep you on track.

You can have regular writer's workshops with your fellow writers-whether it be classmates, friends, family, or a local writers' group, You can also share your work online, either privately with a select few or publicly, depending on your comfort level. On the next page, there's a list of easy-to-use, free blogging sites where you can publish your work, if you so choose.

FREE BLOGGING SITES

You can certainly open up a word processing document or get a nice a blank notebook and write there. However, you may want to share your work. Or, if you are a teacher, you may want your students to be able to share. A blog is a wonderful way to post fiction online for others to see. Most blogs allow you to format your title, add pictures, or link to other sites. They often have spell-check which is quite useful. Finally, many blog platforms allow you to control who sees your work, allowing you to open it up only to your classmates or a small group of friends or fellow writers.

Here is a list of some popular, free, blogging sites.

1. Facebook: While it's known as a social-media site, you can also post long pieces if you want to. You can control the privacy settings of each individual post. Or you can create a private page for your writing. You may even want to make a group with your fellow writers.

2. WordPress.com: Fairly easy to use with lots of customization options. There are free and paid options, but the free plan is all you need to start writing online. There are a lot of tools to make it easy to share on social media.

3. Blogger: Google's blog software is well-known and widely used. The free version has ads, but it's much easier to use than WordPress.

4. Tumblr: While best-known for image sharing, Tumblr can be used as a blogging site as well. It's easy to follow your friends' blogs too.

5. LiveJournal: A Russian-owned blogging site that also puts an emphasis on community, making it easy to post and also follow what others are up to.

6. Medium: You may follow a well-known influencer on Medium, but the platform is actually open to everyone for free!

7. Instagram: Another social media site that can be used for longer text posts. Instagram requires a picture for every post. However, it can be inspirational to find a photo to match your writing. Or turn the prompt into an image!

Name: _____   Date: _____

Tell me a Story About . . .

A genie that grants wishes by taking things away from other people.

- What could go wrong?
- Could some good come out of this?
- What would you wish for?
- What would you hope no one would take from you?

_____

_____

_____

_____

_____

_____

_____

_____

_____

_____

_____

_____

_____

_____

_____

_____

_____

_____

_____

_____

Name: _____   Date: _____

Tell me a Story About . . .

A notebook that makes everything you write in it come true.

- What would write in a notebook like that?
- What's the best thing this notebook could do?
- What's the worst thing that could go wrong?

_____

_____

_____

_____

_____

_____

_____

_____

_____

_____

_____

_____

_____

_____

_____

_____

_____

_____

_____

_____

_____

Name: _____   Date: _____

Tell me a Story About . . .

A world in which different places exist in different periods of time.

- How do people travel?
- What if your friends or family lived in your past?
- What else might be true of this world?

_____

_____

_____

_____

_____

_____

_____

_____

_____

_____

_____

_____

_____

_____

_____

_____

_____

_____

_____

_____

_____

Name: _____   Date: _____

Tell me a Story About . . .

A person who wakes up to find that no one knows who they are.

- Or maybe no one knows who anyone is.
- What happened to cause this?
- How will it be resolved?

_____

_____

_____

_____

_____

_____

_____

_____

_____

_____

_____

_____

_____

_____

_____

_____

_____

_____

_____

_____

_____

_____

_____

Name: _____   Date: _____

Tell me a Story About . . .

A group of people who find out the real meaning of life.

- Who will they tell?
- Will anyone believe them?
- Could this knowledge have negative effects on the people or the world?
- Who might want to stop them?
- What is the real meaning of life?

_____

_____

_____

_____

_____

_____

_____

_____

_____

_____

_____

_____

_____

_____

_____

_____

_____

_____

_____

Name: _____   Date: _____

Tell me a Story About . . .

A store that sells anything the customer wants, real or imagined.

- What would you want?
- What's the weirdest thing someone might get from the store?
- Are there any rules or limits to what people can get?
- How did this store come to be?

_____
_____
_____
_____
_____
_____
_____
_____
_____
_____
_____
_____
_____
_____
_____
_____
_____
_____
_____
_____
_____
_____
_____

Name: _____   Date: _____

Tell me a Story About . . .

A man who discovers his wife of ten years is actually a robot.

- Or an alien, clone, werewolf, vampire, witch, etc...
- Will he accept this in the end or leave her?
- How will she react to his reaction?
- Will you set your story in the real world, or will she pull him into an alternative world?

_____

_____

_____

_____

_____

_____

_____

_____

_____

_____

_____

_____

_____

_____

_____

_____

_____

_____

_____

Name: _____   Date: _____

Tell me a Story About . . .

A person who makes all their choices in life by flipping a coin.

- What's the best thing that could happen?
- What's the worst?
- Would there be any decisions he would chose not to make this way?
- Why are they doing this?

Name: _____   Date: _____

Tell me a Story About . . .

A self-driving car that decides people need to have more fun in life.

- What would it do to help people enjoy life?
- Will people see this as helpful or annoying?
- What happened to make the car feel this way?

_____

_____

_____

_____

_____

_____

_____

_____

_____

_____

_____

_____

_____

_____

_____

_____

_____

_____

_____

_____

_____

Tell me a Story About . . .

A man who wakes up in prison in a strange country where he doesn't speak the language.

- How did he get there?
- How will he get out?
- How can he survive there?
- Where is the prison and what language do they speak?

_____

_____

_____

_____

_____

_____

_____

_____

_____

_____

_____

_____

_____

_____

_____

_____

_____

_____

_____

_____

_____

_____

_____

Tell me a Story About . . .

A demon who wants to make up for all the bad things they've done.

- Will his supervisors notice?
- Will any other spiritual beings notice?
- Will he start doing good things or make amends to his previous victims or something else?
- Will people trust him?

_____

_____

_____

_____

_____

_____

_____

_____

_____

_____

_____

_____

_____

_____

_____

_____

_____

_____

_____

_____

_____

_____

_____

Tell me a Story About . . .

A ghost haunting a house that one day burns down.

- Why was he haunting the house?
- Can ghosts move to a new house?
- Is this story a horror story or a comedy or both?

_____

_____

_____

_____

_____

_____

_____

_____

_____

_____

_____

_____

_____

_____

_____

_____

_____

_____

_____

_____

_____

Name: _____   Date: _____

Tell me a Story About . . .

A magic book that writes down everything you say and do, no matter how good or bad.

- How might this book be used? How could it be abused?
- Is this a unique book or does everyone have one?
- Who made it and why and how?
- Does this world have other magic devices?

_____

_____

_____

_____

_____

_____

_____

_____

_____

_____

_____

_____

_____

_____

_____

_____

_____

_____

_____

_____

_____

Tell me a Story About . . .

A woman who meets herself but at a different age.

- Is it a younger or older self? Or maybe a self from another dimension?
- Is this a story about time-travel, clones, or visions, or something else?
- Is her other self aware that they are the same person?
- What lessons could she teach her other self or her other self teach her?

_____
_____
_____
_____
_____
_____
_____
_____
_____
_____
_____
_____
_____
_____
_____
_____
_____
_____
_____
_____
_____
_____
_____

Name: _____   Date: _____

Tell me a Story About . . .

An AI that decides the best way to help people is to control the whole world.

- Does the AI succeed or fail?
- Do people become aware and fight back?
- Is the AI right?
- What's the moral of this story?

_____

_____

_____

_____

_____

_____

_____

_____

_____

_____

_____

_____

_____

_____

_____

_____

_____

_____

_____

_____

Tell me a Story About . . .

A world in which all jobs are done by computers and robots.

- What do people do instead of working?
- Is this a utopia or a dystopia?
- Are computers good at our jobs?
- Do some jobs disappear?
- What are the consequences for working?

_____

_____

_____

_____

_____

_____

_____

_____

_____

_____

_____

_____

_____

_____

_____

_____

_____

_____

_____

_____

Name: _____   Date: _____

Tell me a Story About . . .

A group of doctors who have the power to decide who gets medical treatment and who doesn't.

- Who chose these doctors?
- How do they make their choices?
- What cases do they hear?
- Do they ever make mistakes?

_____

_____

_____

_____

_____

_____

_____

_____

_____

_____

_____

_____

_____

_____

_____

_____

_____

_____

_____

_____

_____

Tell me a Story About . . .

A library that contains every book every written, real or imaginary.

- What's the most interesting book in this library?
- Could there be a book there that someone doesn't want to exist?
- Is there a famous book that could have a mistake in it?
- Who gets to go to this library? What are the rules?
- What could threaten the existence of the library?

Name: _____   Date: _____

Tell me a Story About . . .

A mirror that lets you see what is happening anywhere in the world but only for 60 seconds.

- If you had a mirror like that, what would you want to see?
- What would you NOT want to see?
- What would you not want SEEN?
- Can the mirror see the past or the future or only the present?
- Is the mirror always correct?

_____

_____

_____

_____

_____

_____

_____

_____

_____

_____

_____

_____

_____

_____

_____

_____

_____

_____

_____

_____

Name: _____   Date: _____

Tell me a Story About . . .

A house elf who gets fed up with helping people all the time.

- Why are they tired of their job?
- What does the house elf want to do instead?
- Does the house elf want some kind of revenge?
- What will happen to the people the elf was helping?

_____

_____

_____

_____

_____

_____

_____

_____

_____

_____

_____

_____

_____

_____

_____

_____

_____

_____

_____

_____

_____

_____

_____

_____

Name: _____   Date: _____

Tell me a Story About . . .

A person who feels the emotions of the people around him, but not their thoughts.

- How did they discover their power?
- Does the person want to use their power or try to get rid of it?
- How could they use it to help people or hurt people?

_____

_____

_____

_____

_____

_____

_____

_____

_____

_____

_____

_____

_____

_____

_____

_____

_____

_____

_____

_____

Tell me a Story About . . .

A world where boys are encouraged to do traditionally girlish things like play house, while girls are encouraged to do boyish things like sports and roughhousing.

- Is the way it's always been or was there a change?
- Are other social roles different?
- What lessons could this world teach us about our society?
- Is everyone happy with this arrangement?
- What are the other alternatives for gender-roles?

Name: _____   Date: _____

Tell me a Story About . . .

An angel who discovers a terrible flaw in the creation.

- What is the flaw and what are the consequences?
- How do they discover it?
- Who knows about it?
- Where did the flaw come from?
- Can the flaw be fixed or resolved in some way?

Name: _____   Date: _____

Tell me a Story About . . .

An infallible love detector that can tell you if your relationship will work out or not.

- Would you want to take such a test?
- What would happen if you took this test and found out you were incompatible?
- Could there be a downside to the love detector saying your relationship is perfect?
- Who might control this device?
- What kind of couple would love or hate this kind of device?

_____

_____

_____

_____

_____

_____

_____

_____

_____

_____

_____

_____

_____

_____

_____

_____

_____

_____

_____

_____

_____

_____

Name: _____ Date: _____

Tell me a Story About . . .

A pen that will not write something down if it is not true?

- Who owns this pen and what do they do with it?
- What are some ways this pen could be useful?
- What are some ways it could be terrible?
- Is there any way to deceive it?
- What happens to the writings?

_____

_____

_____

_____

_____

_____

_____

_____

_____

_____

_____

_____

_____

_____

_____

_____

_____

_____

_____

_____

Name: _____   Date: _____

Tell me a Story About . . .

A country where citizens are chosen at random to be supreme leader for a month.

- What would you do if you were supreme leader?
- What kinds of conflicts might there be?
- Could someone rig the system?
- Are there any rules or limits?

_____

_____

_____

_____

_____

_____

_____

_____

_____

_____

_____

_____

_____

_____

_____

_____

_____

_____

_____

_____

_____

Name: _____   Date: _____

Tell me a Story About . . .

A salon that can change your appearance in any way you can imagine.

- What would you want to look like?
- Could this ability be used to hurt or help people?
- Are there are rules or limits to this?

_____

_____

_____

_____

_____

_____

_____

_____

_____

_____

_____

_____

_____

_____

_____

_____

_____

_____

_____

_____

_____

_____

Name: _____   Date: _____

Tell me a Story About . . .

An assistant who suspects their boss is a vampire.

- Or a zombie, alien, robot, clone, etc...
- What happened to make the assistant suspicious?
- How will they test their theory?
- Is their boss a vampire or maybe something else unusual?
- Is this a comedy or a horror story?

_____
_____
_____
_____
_____
_____
_____
_____
_____
_____
_____
_____
_____
_____
_____
_____
_____
_____
_____
_____
_____

Name: _____   Date: _____

Tell me a Story About . . .

- **A world in which days are long and go through seasons.**
- What words do people use to talk about days in this world?
- How is eating, working, sleeping organized?
- How does it affect people's sense of history?

_____
_____
_____
_____
_____
_____
_____
_____
_____
_____
_____
_____
_____
_____
_____
_____
_____
_____
_____
_____
_____

Tell me a Story About . . .

Choose an important historical event and create a world where that event didn't happen.

- What event will you chose?
- What are the consequences? Who is affected by the consequences?
- What happened instead?
- What is unusual about this world as a result of this different history?
- What can we learn about this event and its impact on the real world from your story?

_____

_____

_____

_____

_____

_____

_____

_____

_____

_____

_____

_____

_____

_____

_____

_____

_____

_____

_____

_____

Name: _____   Date: _____

Tell me a Story About . . .

An artist who paints what your soul looks like.

- Would you like to see your soul?
- What kind of people would like to see their soul or hate to see it?
- What differences might there be between what your soul looks like and what you look like?
- How might this ability be used or abused?

_____

_____

_____

_____

_____

_____

_____

_____

_____

_____

_____

_____

_____

_____

_____

_____

_____

_____

_____

_____

_____

Tell me a Story About . . .

A robot servant that can read your mind to give you what you want at all times.

- What are the benefits of having such a servant?
- What are the disadvantages?
- What else might the robot know about you?
- What might someone do if they could read your mind?

_____

_____

_____

_____

_____

_____

_____

_____

_____

_____

_____

_____

_____

_____

_____

_____

_____

_____

_____

_____

_____

_____

Name: _____   Date: _____

Tell me a Story About . . .

A person who discovers their parents made a deal with the devil.

- Or another family member or friend.
- What was the deal? Why was it made?
- How does it affect this person's life?
- What kind of person is the devil in this story?
- Will the deal be fulfilled or is there a way out of it?

_____

_____

_____

_____

_____

_____

_____

_____

_____

_____

_____

_____

_____

_____

_____

_____

_____

_____

_____

_____

Tell me a Story About . . .

A pair of twins who can read each other's minds, no matter how far away they are.

- How might they use this power to help or hurt people?
- Are there any limits to the power?
- Does anyone know about it?
- What kinds of dangers could they face?

_____

_____

_____

_____

_____

_____

_____

_____

_____

_____

_____

_____

_____

_____

_____

_____

_____

_____

_____

_____

_____

_____

Name: _____   Date: _____

Tell me a Story About . . .

A mail delivery gone wrong.

- Is this a comedy, mystery, horror, thriller, or romance?
- What was in the mail and what went wrong?
- Was the delivery lost, went to the wrong person, was opened by mistake?
- Who has to fix the mistake and how will they do it?

_____

_____

_____

_____

_____

_____

_____

_____

_____

_____

_____

_____

_____

_____

_____

_____

_____

_____

_____

_____

_____

_____

Name: _____   Date: _____

Tell me a Story About . . .

A smartphone that can make calls for you in your voice.

- How would this be useful?
- How could this be abused?
- What if the cellphone became intelligent?
- What kinds of laws might there be about this?

_____

_____

_____

_____

_____

_____

_____

_____

_____

_____

_____

_____

_____

_____

_____

_____

_____

_____

_____

_____

Tell me a Story About . . .

A police officer who refuses to use violence.

- How do they protect themselves?
- Why do they have this belief?
- What problems could it cause?
- What are the benefits of this belief?

_____

_____

_____

_____

_____

_____

_____

_____

_____

_____

_____

_____

_____

_____

_____

_____

_____

_____

_____

_____

Name: _____   Date: _____

Tell me a Story About . . .

_____
_____
_____
_____
_____
_____
_____
_____
_____
_____
_____
_____
_____
_____
_____
_____
_____
_____
_____
_____
_____
_____

Name: _____   Date: _____

Tell me a Story About . . .

A house that lets you live forever, but you can never leave it.

- Who owns the house and how did they find it?
- What kind of person might want to live in this house? Would you?
- What problems could it cause?
- What happens when people leave?

_____
_____
_____
_____
_____
_____
_____
_____
_____
_____
_____
_____
_____
_____
_____
_____
_____
_____
_____
_____

Name: _____   Date: _____

Tell me a Story About . . .

A world in which teleporting is cheap and easy.

- How are families and friendships different?
- What effect does it have on international relations?
- Imagine a fantasy day where you teleport all over the world. Where do you go and what do you do?

_____

_____

_____

_____

_____

_____

_____

_____

_____

_____

_____

_____

_____

_____

_____

_____

_____

_____

_____

_____

Name: _____   Date: _____

Tell me a Story About . . .

A computer program that can instantly teach you one skill.

- What skill would you like to learn?
- Where might this program be used and for what?
- What would happen if the wrong person had access to this program?
- Would there be any side effects of using it too much?
- What if everyone had the same skill?

Name: _____   Date: _____

Tell me a Story About . . .

A job that pays you in dreams.

- What is your happiest dream?
- What kind of job is this? Who is the employer?
- How does company put dreams in your head?
- What else might use dreams as currency in this world?

_____

_____

_____

_____

_____

_____

_____

_____

_____

_____

_____

_____

_____

_____

_____

_____

_____

_____

_____

_____

_____

Name: _____   Date: _____

Tell me a Story About . . .

A telephone that allows you to call anyone, dead or alive, real or imaginary.

- Who would you call?
- Is the telephone always accurate?
- How does it work? Are there any rules or limitations?
- What's the weirdest thing you can imagine doing with the telephone?
- Who controls the phone and what happens if they lose control?

_____

_____

_____

_____

_____

_____

_____

_____

_____

_____

_____

_____

_____

_____

_____

_____

_____

_____

_____

_____

Tell me a Story About . . .

A musical instrument that plays everyone's favorite song.

- Who might own this instrument?
- What are some good and bad things one might do with it?
- Can you think of a fairy tale with a magical instrument in it?
- Who made this instrument and how did it come to be?

_____

_____

_____

_____

_____

_____

_____

_____

_____

_____

_____

_____

_____

_____

_____

_____

_____

_____

_____

_____

Name: _____   Date: _____

Tell me a Story About . . .

A key that can open any door.

- What secrets might someone keep behind a locked door? What would happen if one of those secrets was revealed?
- What might someone keep captive behind a door and what if it got out?
- What other kinds of things could be doors?
- Where could doors go besides rooms?
- Where would this key have come from?

_____

_____

_____

_____

_____

_____

_____

_____

_____

_____

_____

_____

_____

_____

_____

_____

_____

_____

_____

_____

_____

Name: _____   Date: _____

Tell me a Story About . . .

The perfect crime.

- How was it done?
- Why did the person get away with it?
- What benefit did the criminal get from their crime?
- Will anyone ever figure it out?

_____

_____

_____

_____

_____

_____

_____

_____

_____

_____

_____

_____

_____

_____

_____

_____

_____

_____

_____

_____

_____

_____

Name: _____   Date: _____

Tell me a Story About . . .

An alien who comes to Earth during a big holiday celebration.

- What holiday and what is happening?
- What will the alien think is happening?
- What could the alien misunderstand about our life here?
- Will the alien like the celebration or not?

_____

_____

_____

_____

_____

_____

_____

_____

_____

_____

_____

_____

_____

_____

_____

_____

_____

_____

_____

_____

Name: _____ Date: _____

Tell me a Story About . . .

A world that is about to end?

- How will it end and why?
- Does anyone know?
- What are people doing to get ready or try to prevent the end of the world?
- What will happen after the end of the world

_____

_____

_____

_____

_____

_____

_____

_____

_____

_____

_____

_____

_____

_____

_____

_____

_____

_____

_____

_____

_____

Name: _____   Date: _____

Tell me a Story About . . .

A magic wand that can bring the dead back for only 2 hours.

- Who would you want to bring back?
- What could someone do in 2 hours?
- What secrets could someone learn from a dead person?
- Are there any famous people that could be used in some way?

_____

_____

_____

_____

_____

_____

_____

_____

_____

_____

_____

_____

_____

_____

_____

_____

_____

_____

_____

_____

Tell me a Story About . . .

Thought police who can read your mind.

- What will be the punishment for thought crimes? Will it be the same as doing the crime itself?
- What kinds of thoughts will be illegal?
- What kinds of mistakes or complications could this system have?
- How exactly would it work?
- Who would be monitoring the thoughts? How would they feel?

_____

_____

_____

_____

_____

_____

_____

_____

_____

_____

_____

_____

_____

_____

_____

_____

_____

_____

_____

_____

Name: _____   Date: _____

Tell me a Story About . . .

A person wakes up after having been frozen for 100 years.

- Why were they frozen?
- What are the biggest differences in the world now?
- What's the first thing they would do?
- What important events have they missed?
- How do they feel?

_____

_____

_____

_____

_____

_____

_____

_____

_____

_____

_____

_____

_____

_____

_____

_____

_____

_____

_____

_____

Name: _____   Date: _____

Tell me a Story About . . .

A leader of a country who takes one phone call a day from an ordinary citizen.

- What kinds of things do people say to the leader?
- What is the weirdest thing that could happen on a phone call?
- How did this system come to be?
- How do they choose who gets to call?
- How do you think the leader feels about this?

_____
_____
_____
_____
_____
_____
_____
_____
_____
_____
_____
_____
_____
_____
_____
_____
_____
_____
_____
_____
_____

OTHER WRITING JOURNALS FROM ALPHABET PUBLISHING

Reflections Weekly Writing Journal:

52 Prompts about You

Agree or Disagree: 52 Writing Prompts
for Opinion Essays

Comparisons: 52 Writing Prompts for

Compare/Contrast Essays

Case Studies: 52 Writing Prompts for

Problem/Solution Essays

Draw and Write: Writing Journal for

Young Learners

Picture Prompts Writing Journal

www.alphabetpublishingbooks.com

We are a small, independent publishing company that specializes in creative resource
for teachers in the area of English Language Arts and English as a Second or Othe
Language. We help stock the teacher toolkit with practical, useful, and innovativ

CPSIA information can be obtained
at www.ICGtesting.com
Printed in the USA
FSHW012050180122
87759FS